# GREAT LEGS
## IN 10 MINUTES A DAY

### Deborah Frichman-McKenzie

SCHOLASTIC INC.
New York Toronto London Auckland Sydney Tokyo

I dedicate this book to my mother and father who
taught me the meaning of good health and a good life
with the greatest gift of all: LOVE.

ISBN: 0-590-42023-2

12 11 10 9 8 7 6 5 4 3 2 1                                    8 9/8 0 1 2 3/9

Printed in the U.S.A.

# GREAT LEGS
## IN 10
## MINUTES
## A DAY

# INTRODUCTION

The Great Legs in 10 Minutes A Day program is designed to help you get your legs in the best shape possible in the least amount of time. The exercises in this book are easy to learn and can be fun to do, especially if you let yourself really get into the movements. There's only one catch to the program: you have to *do* the exercises, every day, and not just look at the pictures.

Make this program a regular part of your life; the rewards make it worth your while. The program is designed especially for *you,* the teen with a busy schedule. *Everyone* can spare ten minutes for a quick workout, even on their most hectic days. These exercises are equally effective whether you do them in the morning, after school, in the evening, or right before bedtime. Plan to do the exercises in this program every day at the same time, and *stick with* your plan—you'll be glad you did.

The ten exercises are divided into five categories, and the program should always be followed in order:

### 1—WARM-UPS

### 2—STRETCHES

### 3—SLENDERCISES

### 4—JUMPS

### 5—DANCING TO GREAT LEGS

The routine for each of these categories consists of two exercises, and each exercise is meant to last one minute. Of course, every person exercises at a different pace, but if you find your workout running *far* ahead or behind the ten-minute mark, you should adjust your pace. You may find that you really like the way exercising makes you feel—if so, there is certainly no need to *limit* your workout to ten minutes a day! Expand your daily exercise program to include a daily walk, run, swim, or bicycle ride—these activities are all terrific leg-shapers, as well as being excellent aerobic exercise.

Never skip the Warm-ups, no matter what. They help your body get ready to work out. If you don't do them every time, you'll suffer from aches, pains, and even possible injury to your body. Doing the Warm-ups will help you avoid injury, but as with any new physical activity, it also makes sense to check with your doctor before you start this or any exercise program. The idea is to get your body in shape, not to tear it apart!

The ten exercises that make up this program may *look* simple, but they get results. In the ten minutes it takes to complete this program each day, you will effectively stretch, tone, and strengthen every muscle in your legs as you get them into the best shape they've ever been in. Your legs will feel stronger and look more shapely, within weeks!

In addition to the ten exercises in the program, there is a special section called "Anywhere Exercises." The "Anywheres" are two simple routines that you can do anytime, anywhere. You don't need an exercise mat or special workout clothes for these. There's one for times when you have to stand around (waiting on a movie line, for example), and one for those times when you've got to be sitting quietly. These exercises make a great addition to the basic Great Legs program. Try them—they'll make a difference!

Fashionable exercise clothes can add another dimension to your Great Legs workout. The color and styles of exercise wear are endless; there's plenty of variety to choose from. Many styles make a great addition to any wardrobe, because you can wear them both for working out *and* going out. The key to exercise fashion, as with all fashion, is to make sure you feel comfortable and look good. Some girls like to work out in leotards, some like shorts. Wear whatever feels and looks best to you. You may get some ideas for new outfits from the pictures at the end of the book. Remember, fun workout wear is a great way to keep motivated. If you've got something fresh to wear when you're exercising, the program will seem less like a chore and more like a treat.

Be sure to check out the Discography at the back of this book. There are suggestions for great tunes to work out to. The right music can make all the difference. Working out is less work and more fun when Cindy Lauper or the Talking Heads are around!

Now you're all ready to start your Great Legs program. So put on your favorite exercise wear, turn up the music, and enjoy yourself. Ten minutes a day will:

- Turn flab into lean muscle
- Boost your energy level
- Reduce fatigue and allow you to get *more* out of your life
- Give you sounder, more restful sleep
- Improve your blood circulation
- And, best of all, it will get you:

### GREAT LEGS!

# Warm-Ups

*Two minutes to get you ready to go!*

# Warm-Ups

These two warm-ups are simple movements that will loosen up your body and warm up your muscles. As with any physical activity, the Great Legs Warm-up prepares you for your best exercise performance. Exercising without warming up is like starting your car on a cold morning and racing straight to the highway.

Your body is your most important possession. Use it with care and safety.

*WARM-UP TIPS:*
- *Breathe in and out continuously*

- *Hold your stomach in throughout the exercises*

- *Don't rush through the exercises*

# The Big Stretch

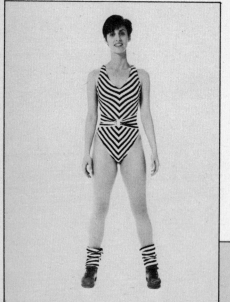

## 1

Start by standing tall with your feet shoulder-width apart and arms at your sides.

## 2

With knees slightly bent to relieve any pressure on your back, bend your torso forward, stretching your hands toward the floor. Continue stretching for an eight count.

**3**

*Keeping your heels on the floor, bend deeply at the knees and grab your ankles.*

**4**

*Holding your grasp, straighten your legs. Bend and straighten this way eight times, then gently roll up until you are back at position 1.*

**5**

*Repeat entire exercise.*

*The Big Stretch is good for the back of the thighs and the back of calves.*

# Leg Risers

**1** *Start with your legs straight and both arms stretched out to the sides.*

**2** Keeping the position, go up and down on your toes.

**3** Repeat entire exercise fifteen times.

*Leg Risers are good for ankles, calves, and front of thighs.*

# Stretches

*Two minutes to make you loose and limber!*

# Stretches

The stretching exercises are designed to lengthen the muscles of your legs. These exercises conclude the work started with the warm-ups. The stretches are designed to stretch the muscles on the front and the back of your legs. When you don't exercise, these muscles can become very stiff. The exercises in this section will lengthen those muscles, and give you longer-looking legs.

*STRETCHING TIPS:*

- *Try to relax*
- *Always breathe in before stretching and breathe out while stretching*
- *Keep your shoulders down — don't let them "hunch up"*
- *Hold your stomach in throughout the exercises*
- *Don't rush*

# The Upside-Down Stretch

**1** *With your fingertips on the floor and your right leg as support, stretch your left leg up diagonally. Continue stretching your leg up for a count of ten.*

**2** Still using your right leg as support, and keeping your left diagonally up, bend both knees. Now, bend and straighten your
legs ten times.

**3** Reverse your position and repeat the entire exercise, using your
left leg as support and stretching your right leg.

*The Upside-Down Stretch is good for back of thighs and calves.*

# Bend and Stretch

**1** Start by sitting on the floor with your legs stretched out to the sides. Your feet should be pointed. Hold your arms stretched out, palms facing downward.

**2** Bend your arms, keeping the palms facing downwards. At the same time, bend your legs and flex your feet.

**3** Repeat entire exercise thirty times.

*The Bend and Stretch is good for front of thighs and ankles.*

# Slendercises

*Two minutes to get
you all toned up!*

# Slendercises

Slendercises are a group of exercises that strengthen specific spots of the legs, which is why they're also known as "spot toning" exercises. These are the exercises that give your legs an attractive shape.

*SLENDERCISES TIPS:*

- *Breathe in and out continuously*
- *Use your muscles — don't just go through the motions*
- *Hold your stomach in throughout the exercises*
- *Keep your back straight*

# The Leg Up

**1** Lie on your right side, resting your head on your right arm. Place your left hand in front as support. Now bend your right knee forward, keeping your left leg stretched out and off the floor.

**2** Raise your left leg as high as you can, keeping the knee facing front.

**3** Repeat entire exercise twenty times on your right side, then reverse your position and repeat entire exercise on your left side.

The Leg Up is good for outside of thigh.

# Scissors

**1** Lie on your right side, legs straight, left leg raised above the floor. Rest your head on your outstretched right arm, placing your left hand on the floor as support.

**2** Without moving your left leg, reach your right leg up to touch it.

**3** Repeat entire exercise twenty times on your right side, then reverse your position and repeat exercise on your left side.

*The Scissors are good for inner thighs.*

# Jumps

*Two minutes to get you energized!*

# Jumps

The Jumps section is the most exciting part of your workout. This is the time for you to release all your energy. The jumps you do here will give you trimmer and more shapely legs.

Choose your favorite songs from the Discography, and really get into it!

*JUMPING TIPS:*

- *Jump with intensity from beginning to end*
- *Always land toe-to-heel*
- *Work out both sides equally*
- *Never hold your breath*
- *Hold your stomach in throughout the jumps*

# Jumping For Joy

**1**

Jump up with both feet
and clap your hands.

**2**

Jump on your right
foot, holding your left
leg out to the side.
Stretch your right arm
up and hold your left
arm to the side as you
jump.

**3**

*Jump up with both feet and clap your hands again.*

**4**

*Jump on your left foot, holding your right leg out to the side. Stretch your left arm up and hold your right arm out to the side as you jump.*

**5**

*Repeat entire exercise twenty times.*

*Jumping for Joy is good for ankles, calves, front of the thighs, and outer thighs.*

# One, Two, Three, Split!

## 1

Bend your left leg up and hop on your right foot three times. Clench your fists and make a choo-choo motion with your arms as you hop.

## 2

Split! *by jumping on both feet and stretching your arms out to the sides.*

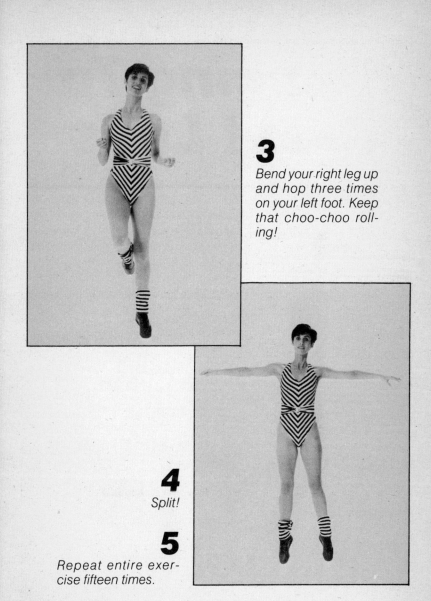

**3**

*Bend your right leg up and hop three times on your left foot. Keep that choo-choo rolling!*

**4**

*Split!*

**5**

*Repeat entire exercise fifteen times.*

*One, Two, Three, Split is good for entire leg and ankles.*

# Dancing To Great Legs

*Two minutes of pure fun!*

# Dancing To Great Legs

The exercises in this section are a combination of body movements, united rhythmically in dancelike patterns. Dancing To Great Legs is your chance to bring out the dancer inside you. What could be better than dancing inches away to your favorite song? This chapter not only ends your workout in a fun way, but also works as a cool-down.

Don't be shy! Loosen up and have fun!

*DANCING TIPS:*

- *Give special attention to your breathing — breathe in and out continuously*
- *Stay loose as you do these exercises*
- *Let your mind and body get into the music*

# All That Jazz

## 1

Turn to the right, stretching your left arm forward and your right arm back. Keep your right leg bent and stretch your left leg out.

## 2

Reverse the motion by turning to the left. Stretch your right arm forward, your left arm back, and your right leg out.

**3**

*Bend your right leg and stretch your left leg out to the side. Reach your right arm up and your left arm down.*

**4**

*Reverse the movement by bending your left leg and stretching your right leg out to the side. Reach your left arm up, and your right arm down.*

**5**

*Repeat entire exercise twelve times.*

*All That Jazz is good for front of thighs and inner thighs.*

# Quadrokick

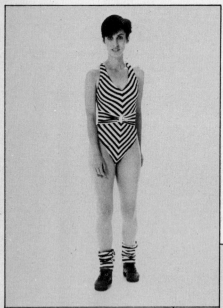

## 1

Take four steps forward, right foot first.

## 2

Shake your right leg out in front four times in a fluid kicking motion.

**3**

*Shake your right leg back four times in a fluid kicking motion.*

**4**

*Take four steps backwards, right foot first, to original position.*

**5**

*Repeat entire exercise four times, then reverse and repeat, kicking with your left leg.*

*The Quadrokick is good for cooling down all muscles in the leg.*

# Anywhere Exercises

The Anywhere Exercises are simple exercises that do not require a specific place or special attention. They can be done anytime, anywhere, without interfering with what you're doing. Try them while you're waiting in the movie line, sitting on the bus, or watching TV.

*ANYWHERE TIPS:*

- *Keep your back straight*
- *Keep your stomach pulled in throughout the exercises*
- *Do these as often as possible throughout the day*

# The Pivot and Bend

(Try this one when you're standing on line.)

**1** Standing straight and tall, pivot your feet from the ankles so that only the outsides of your feet touch the floor and support your weight.

**2** Pivot your feet at the ankles so that only the insides of your feet touch the floor and support your weight.

**3** Put your feet flat on the floor and bend both knees, keeping your back straight.

**4** Straighten your legs to take you back to standing position.

**5** Repeat ten times.

*The Pivot and Bend exercise is good for thighs, ankles, and calves.*

# Foot Ups

(Try this one when you're sitting at a desk.)

**1** Sit up straight with your feet apart. Fully flex your feet until only your heels touch the floor.

**2** Lower your toes, pointing your feet, until your heels are fully raised and only your toes touch the floor.

**3** Repeat ten times.

*Foot Ups are good for calves and ankles.*

# Fashion Tips for Great Legs

*If you have short legs:*
Avoid wearing long shorts and dresses or skirts that drape below the knee. They will make your legs look shorter. You are better off wearing dresses, skirts, and shorts that are cut above the knee, since the more leg you expose the longer your legs will appear to be.

*If you have large thighs:*
Avoid wearing tight pants, since they will only emphasize your problem areas. Similarly, fancy designs or bright colors call too much attention to all the wrong places. Try wearing some of the new baggy pants, or try long pleated skirts.

*If you have large calves:*
Avoid wearing knee socks, especially brightly-colored knee-highs, since tight clothing always calls attention to the area of the body it clings to. Remember that high heels tighten the calf muscle and will exaggerate the size of the calf. The smartest fashion look for you is longer dresses and loose pants. Either one will divert attention from your problem areas, and allow your better features to shine through.

And be sure to keep doing your Great Legs program daily. It won't be long until your legs look great in *anything*.

# EXERCISE FASHION

Fashion can help you get into the mood for your Great Legs in 10 Minutes a Day program. The popularity of exercise means that designers have created a whole new world of exciting fashion for you to play in. They are making jumpsuits, leotards, tights, and shorts in a rainbow of colors, for every budget. The best footwear for exercise is light-weight and supportive shoes like sneakers or dance shoes. The clothes shown here are a cross section of the ever-growing world of designs available. Most exercise wear is a good buy, because it can be worn both as workout wear and for casual wear around town.

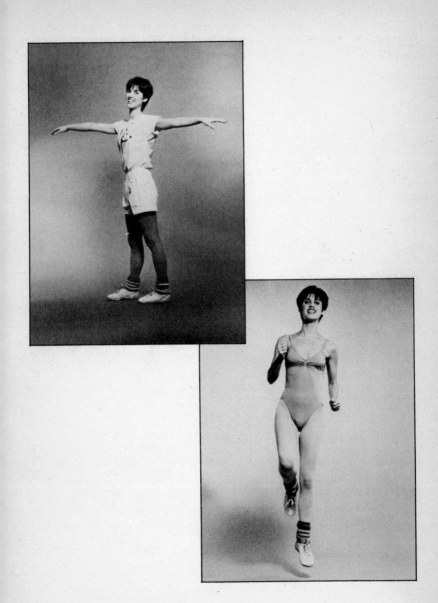

GREAT LEGS — Exercise. Fashion

# DISCOGRAPHY

These upbeat songs are the best for Jumps and Dancing To Great Legs.

| SONG TITLE | ARTIST | ALBUM TITLE AND RECORD CO. |
| --- | --- | --- |
| Hit Me With Your Best Shot | Pat Benatar | Crimes of Passion (Chrysalis) |
| We Got The Beat | Go Go's | Beauty & The Beat (RCA) |
| Burning Up | Madonna | Madonna (Sire) |
| Life During War Time | Talking Heads | Fear Of Music (Sire) |
| Upside Down | Diana Ross | Diana (Motown) |
| Head Over Heels | Go Go's | Talk Show (A&M) |
| Rebel Yell | Billy Idol | Rebel Yell (Chrysalis) |
| The Heart Of Rock & Roll | Huey Lewis and The News | Sports (Chrysalis) |
| I Want A New Drug | Huey Lewis and The News | Sports (Chrysalis) |

Pat Benatar

Huey Lewis

| SONG TITLE | ARTIST | ALBUM TITLE AND RECORD CO. |
| --- | --- | --- |
| Girls Just Want To Have Fun | Cindy Lauper | She's So Unusual (Portrait/CBS) |
| Turn The Beat Around | Vicki Sue Robinson | Never Gonna Let You Go (RCA) |
| Let's Go Crazy | Prince and The Revolution | Purple Rain (WB) |
| Dancing In The Dark | Bruce Springsteen | Born In The U.S.A. (Columbia) |
| Who Can It Be Now | Men At Work | Business As Usual (CBS) |
| Relax | Frankie Goes To Hollywood | Welcome To The Pleasure Dome (Island) |
| The Wild Boys | Duran Duran | Duran Duran (EMI) |
| The War Song | Culture Club | Waking up With The House On Fire (Epic) |
| Physical | Olivia Newton-John | Greatest Hits Vol II (MCA) |

Olivia Newton-John

David Byrne of Talking Heads

These songs will give you the right beat for Warm-ups, Stretches, and Slendercises.

| SONG TITLE | ARTIST | ALBUM TITLE AND RECORD CO. |
|---|---|---|
| Work That Body | Diana Ross | Why Do Fools Fall In Love (RCA) |
| On The Radio | Donna Summer | Greatest Hits Vol I & II (Casablanca) |
| Keep The Fire Burning | REO Speedwagon | Good Trouble (Epic) |
| Sarah | Fleetwood Mac | Tusk (WB) |
| Holiday | Madonna | Madonna (Sire) |
| Leave A Tender Moment Alone | Billy Joel | Innocent Man (CBS) |
| Uptown Girl | Billy Joel | Innocent Man (CBS) |
| Come Back and Stay | Paul Young | Paul Young (CBS) |
| I Can't Go For That | Hall & Oates | Private Eyes (RCA) |
| It's So Easy | Linda Ronstadt | Greatest Hits Vol II (Asylum) |
| Material Girl | Madonna | Like A Virgin (Sire) |
| Poison Arrow | ABC | The Lexicon Of Love (Phonogram) |
| The Reflex | Duran Duran | Seven And The Ragged Tiger (EMI) |
| Crumblin' Down | John Cougar | John Cougar Mellencamp (Riva) |
| Sad Songs Say So Much | Elton John | Breaking Hearts (Geffen Records) |
| Every Breath You Take | Police | Synchronicity (A&M) |
| Wrapped Around Your Finger | Police | Synchronicity (A&M) |
| Out Of Touch | Hall & Oates | Big Bam Boom (RCA) |
| Born In The U.S.A. | Bruce Springsteen | Born In The U.S.A. (Columbia) |
| Valotte | Julian Lennon | Valotte (Atlantic) |

# Your Great Legs Progress & Reward Chart

Start TODAY and give yourself a + for every day that you do your Great Legs in 10 Minutes A Day workout. Set a goal of ten consecutive days that you will do the exercises, and pencil in a reward that you will give or do for yourself when you achieve your goal. Keep creating new goals for consistency, rewarding yourself as you go, until the 10 Minutes A Day program becomes a part of your daily life.

In the column for Anywhere Exercises, give yourself a * for every day that you used the simple routines that comprise the Anywhere group. The Anywhere Exercises are an easy way to speed up your progress to the ultimate goal—GREAT LEGS!

| DAY | 10 MINUTE PROGRAM | ANYWHERE EXERCISES | REWARD |
|-----|-------------------|--------------------|--------|
| 1 | | | |
| 2 | | | |
| 3 | | | |
| 4 | | | |
| 5 | | | |
| 6 | | | |
| 7 | | | |
| 8 | | | |

| DAY | 10 MINUTE PROGRAM | ANYWHERE EXERCISES | REWARD |
|-----|-------------------|--------------------|--------|
| 9   |                   |                    |        |
| 10  |                   |                    |        |
| 11  |                   |                    |        |
| 12  |                   |                    |        |
| 13  |                   |                    |        |
| 14  |                   |                    |        |
| 15  |                   |                    |        |
| 16  |                   |                    |        |
| 17  |                   |                    |        |
| 18  |                   |                    |        |
| 19  |                   |                    |        |
| 20  |                   |                    |        |
| 21  |                   |                    |        |
| 22  |                   |                    |        |
| 23  |                   |                    |        |
| 24  |                   |                    |        |
| 25  |                   |                    |        |

# Average Weight for American Females

| HEIGHT (Feet/Inches) | | WEIGHT (Pounds) |
|:---:|:---:|:---:|
| 5 | 0 | 85-100 |
| 5 | 1 | 90-105 |
| 5 | 2 | 95-110 |
| 5 | 3 | 100-115 |
| 5 | 4 | 105-120 |
| 5 | 5 | 110-125 |
| 5 | 6 | 115-130 |
| 5 | 7 | 120-135 |
| 5 | 8 | 124-140 |
| 5 | 9 | 130-145 |
| 5 | 10 | 135-150 |
| 5 | 11 | 140-155 |
| 6 | 0 | 145-160 |

# *About the Author*

Deborah Frichman-McKenzie is the author of *Sexy Legs* and *Shape Your Waist & Hips*, both of which books were translated into Spanish, Swedish, and German. A native of Rio de Janeiro, Brazil, Deborah came to America to study dance with Alvin Ailey and the American Ballet Theatre Company, training she has applied to her exercise programs. Deborah's work has been featured in *Harper's Bazaar, American Photographer, Popular Photography, Seventeen, New Body, The Star,* and numerous other leading periodicals internationally. She has appeared on numerous television talk shows and was recently the subject of a twelve-minute special on dance/exercise for the ABC Television network.